The Little Golden Book of
HYMNS

Compiled by
ELSA JANE WERNER and E.D. EBSUN

Illustrated by
FRANCES SCORE MITCHELL

A GOLDEN BOOK • NEW YORK

Western Publishing Company, Inc., Racine, Wisconsin 53404

Acknowledgments

The publishers wish to thank the following publishers and copyright owners for permission to use hymns in this book: Elizabeth McE. Shields for "A Prayer for Help" from *Worship and Conduct Songs*. Lorenz Publishing Co. for "Joy in Every Heart," copyright Tullar-Meredith Co. "Flowers Below and Stars Above" from *Religion-in-the-Kindergarten* by Bertha Marilda Rhodes; copyright 1924 by the University of Chicago; renewed 1951 by Bertha Marilda Rhodes; reprinted by permission of Harper & Row, Publishers, Inc. Words and music of "Evening Prayer" copyright 1935 by Presbyterian Board of Christian Education; renewed 1963; from *When the Little Child Wants to Sing*; reprinted by permission of The Westminster Press. The Pilgrim Press for "All Things Bright and Beautiful" from *Songs for Little People* by Danielson and Conant.

A Prayer for Help

Elizabeth McE. Shields

Claude T. Curr

Help us, Fa-ther, to re-mem-ber What you'd like to have us do;

Help us to be strong and lov-ing, Help us to be true.

This Is the Day

Psalms 118:24

Charles Cushing

This is the day which the Lord hath made;

We will re- joice_____ and be glad in it.

smoothly

broadening

All Things Bright and Beautiful

Cecil Frances Alexander

Danish Folk Song

Each lit - tle flower that o - pens, Each lit - tle bird that
The pur - ple - head - ed moun - tain, The riv - er run - ning
The cold winds in the win - ter, The pleas - ant sum - mer
He gave us eyes to see___ them, And lips that we might

sings, God made their glow - ing col - ors, He made their ti - ny wings.
by, The sun - set and the morn - ing red, That bright - en up the sky.
sun, The ripe fruits in the gar - den, He made them ev - 'ry one.
tell The good - ness of the Fa - ther, Who do - eth all things well.

To God Who Gives Us Daily Bread

M. Rumsey   Orlando Gibbons

To God, who gives us dai - ly bread, A thank - ful song we'll raise,

And pray that He who sends us food Will fill our hearts with praise. A - men.

Joy in Every Heart

Mabel J. Rosemon

M. Isabelle Ritter

Songs of re - joic - ing fill the air, Ring - ing so sweet and clear.
All Na - ture joins the glo - ry song Ris - ing to heav'n to - day,
Come with re - joic - ing, one and all, Come with your pray'r and praise,

Bright - ness and glad - ness ev - 'ry - where Tell us that Sum - mer's here.
Each whis - p'ring breeze that sweeps a - long Bears hap - py notes a - way.
Pray'r that the Fa - ther's bless - ing fall, Praise for these tune-time days.

CHORUS

Joy, joy in ev - 'ry heart With new life a - thrill,

Bright, bright the sun - beams glow, Hours with glo - ry fill;

Praise, praise the Lord a - bove, For these gold - en days.

Praise the Lord, O come and praise the Lord, And tell His won - drous ways.

Flowers Below and Stars Above

Bertha Marilda Rhodes

Old Folk Song

Flow'rs be - low and stars a - bove Ev - er

tell us God is love; Lit - tle chil - dren wake to

say, "Thank you for the glad new day."

Praise to the Lord

Joachim Neander

Stralsund Songbook

Praise to the Lord, the Al - migh - ty, the King of cre - a - tion.

Trust in God, Our Maker

George Wallace Briggs   *Thomas Tallis*

O God, by whom all things were made, Whose hand is o - ver all,
Thou mad - est all the stars in heav'n, The earth, the deep blue sea:
Thy wis - dom is too won - der - ful For me to un - der - stand:

Be - yond Thy care can no man stray, Nor can a spar - row fall.
Thou mad - est man to know Thy love, And so Thou mad - est me.
But this I know, in this I trust, That I am in Thy hand. A - men.

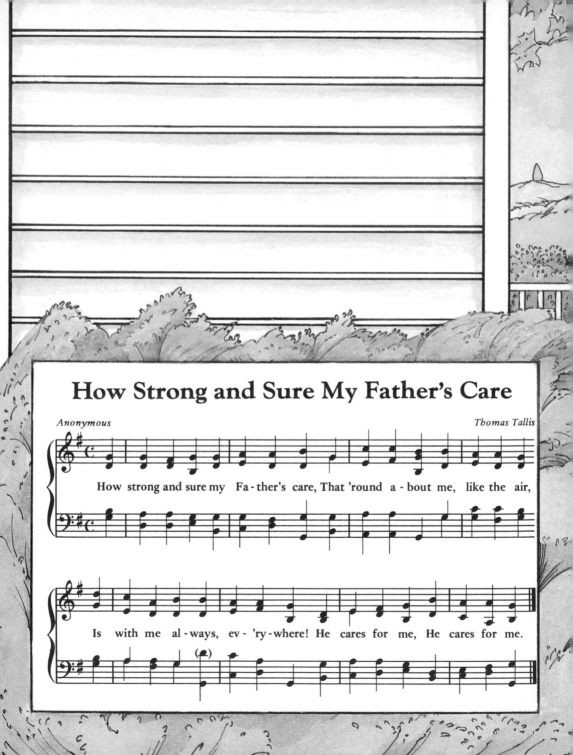

How Strong and Sure My Father's Care

Anonymous

Thomas Tallis

How strong and sure my Fa-ther's care, That 'round a-bout me, like the air,

Is with me al-ways, ev-'ry-where! He cares for me, He cares for me.

Away in a Manger

Words and Music by Martin Luther

Evening Prayer

Anonymous   *Miriam Drury*

Now I lay me down to sleep, I

pray Thee, Lord, Thy child to keep: Thy love guard me

through the night, And wake me with the morn - ing light.